OH MY GOD,
WHAT A COMPLETE DIARY 2023

Gill Books
Hume Avenue
Park West
Dublin 12
www.gillbooks.ie

Gill Books is an imprint of M.H. Gill & Co.
© Emer McLysaght and Sarah Breen 2022
9780717195565

Designed by grahamthew.com
Printed and bound in Turkey by the Imago Group.
This book is typeset in Futura Book.

5 4 3 2 1

THIS DIARY BELONGS TO

- - - - - - - - - - - - - - - - - - - - - - - - - - - - - - - - - - - - - - - - - - - - - - - - - - - - - - - - - - - - - - - -

OH MY GOD,

# What a COMPLETE DIARY 2023

—

EMER McLYSAGHT & SARAH BREEN

—

GILL BOOKS

Happy New Year!

Can you believe it's 2023? We've come so far and been through so much over the past few years and can now look forward to these coming twelve months with some hope and excitement. Maybe even a bit of nervous energy too if you're planning to make a change, take up a new hobby or go on the dream trip you've been putting off!

Excitedly cracking open a brand-new diary in January means yourself and Aisling have at least one thing in common. Even more if you can't fight the instinct to stick your face into its clean, blank pages and inhale deeply. Ahhh! But of course Aisling has been jotting down her thoughts, emotions and feelings on a daily basis long before the concept of 'journaling' or 'practising gratitude' barrelled across the Atlantic (along with baby showers and Krispy Kreme doughnuts). During her teenage years in particular, she found solace in pages just like these, confessing her deepest, darkest secrets (like the time in third year when she knowingly let Sinéad Cloghessy copy the wrong maths homework) and perfecting her signature just in case she eventually found fame as Mrs Shane Filan. She wrote out plenty of angsty song lyrics in her day too, of course.

With that in mind, this year we decided to delve into Aisling's teenage diary archive. You'll find one of these enlightening entries at the start of each new month. As always, each week of the year is spread over two pages and there's a handy section at the end to keep track of your Important Bits as well as plenty of extra space to jot down your thoughts, tot up your annual leave days and still have plenty of room left over to make a list of your enemies. That's what Majella does anyway.

We hope that *Oh My God, What a Complete Diary 2023* becomes a staple on your desk or in your bag and that you find it both entertaining and useful all year long. If you don't, feel free to add us to your own enemies list.

Happy writing!

Emer and Sarah

# 2023 AT A GLANCE

## JANUARY

| M | T | W | T | F | S | S |
|---|---|---|---|---|---|---|
|  |  |  |  |  |  | 1 |
| 2 | 3 | 4 | 5 | 6 | 7 | 8 |
| 9 | 10 | 11 | 12 | 13 | 14 | 15 |
| 16 | 17 | 18 | 19 | 20 | 21 | 22 |
| 23 | 24 | 25 | 26 | 27 | 28 | 29 |
| 30 | 31 |  |  |  |  |  |

## FEBRUARY

| M | T | W | T | F | S | S |
|---|---|---|---|---|---|---|
|  |  | 1 | 2 | 3 | 4 | 5 |
| 6 | 7 | 8 | 9 | 10 | 11 | 12 |
| 13 | 14 | 15 | 16 | 17 | 18 | 19 |
| 20 | 21 | 22 | 23 | 24 | 25 | 26 |
| 27 | 28 |  |  |  |  |  |

## MARCH

| M | T | W | T | F | S | S |
|---|---|---|---|---|---|---|
|  |  | 1 | 2 | 3 | 4 | 5 |
| 6 | 7 | 8 | 9 | 10 | 11 | 12 |
| 13 | 14 | 15 | 16 | 17 | 18 | 19 |
| 20 | 21 | 22 | 23 | 24 | 25 | 26 |
| 27 | 28 | 29 | 30 | 31 |  |  |

## APRIL

| M | T | W | T | F | S | S |
|---|---|---|---|---|---|---|
|  |  |  |  |  | 1 | 2 |
| 3 | 4 | 5 | 6 | 7 | 8 | 9 |
| 10 | 11 | 12 | 13 | 14 | 15 | 16 |
| 17 | 18 | 19 | 20 | 21 | 22 | 23 |
| 24 | 25 | 26 | 27 | 28 | 29 | 30 |

## MAY

| M | T | W | T | F | S | S |
|---|---|---|---|---|---|---|
| 1 | 2 | 3 | 4 | 5 | 6 | 7 |
| 8 | 9 | 10 | 11 | 12 | 13 | 14 |
| 15 | 16 | 17 | 18 | 19 | 20 | 21 |
| 22 | 23 | 24 | 25 | 26 | 27 | 28 |
| 29 | 30 | 31 |  |  |  |  |

## JUNE

| M | T | W | T | F | S | S |
|---|---|---|---|---|---|---|
|  |  |  | 1 | 2 | 3 | 4 |
| 5 | 6 | 7 | 8 | 9 | 10 | 11 |
| 12 | 13 | 14 | 15 | 16 | 17 | 18 |
| 19 | 20 | 21 | 22 | 23 | 24 | 25 |
| 26 | 27 | 28 | 29 | 30 |  |  |

## PUBLIC HOLIDAYS 2023

1 January 2023, Sunday, New Year's Day
6 February 2023, Monday, St Brigid's Day
17 March 2023, Friday, St Patrick's Day

10 April 2023, Monday, Easter Monday
1 May 2023, Monday, May Bank Holiday
5 June 2023, Monday, June Bank Holiday

# 2023 AT A GLANCE

## JULY

| M | T | W | T | F | S | S |
|---|---|---|---|---|---|---|
|   |   |   |   |   | 1 | 2 |
| 3 | 4 | 5 | 6 | 7 | 8 | 9 |
| 10 | 11 | 12 | 13 | 14 | 15 | 16 |
| 17 | 18 | 19 | 20 | 21 | 22 | 23 |
| 24 | 25 | 26 | 27 | 28 | 29 | 30 |
| 31 |   |   |   |   |   |   |

## AUGUST

| M | T | W | T | F | S | S |
|---|---|---|---|---|---|---|
|   | 1 | 2 | 3 | 4 | 5 | 6 |
| 7 | 8 | 9 | 10 | 11 | 12 | 13 |
| 14 | 15 | 16 | 17 | 18 | 19 | 20 |
| 21 | 22 | 23 | 24 | 25 | 26 | 27 |
| 28 | 29 | 30 | 31 |   |   |   |

## SEPTEMBER

| M | T | W | T | F | S | S |
|---|---|---|---|---|---|---|
|   |   |   |   | 1 | 2 | 3 |
| 4 | 5 | 6 | 7 | 8 | 9 | 10 |
| 11 | 12 | 13 | 14 | 15 | 16 | 17 |
| 18 | 19 | 20 | 21 | 22 | 23 | 24 |
| 25 | 26 | 27 | 28 | 29 | 30 |   |

## OCTOBER

| M | T | W | T | F | S | S |
|---|---|---|---|---|---|---|
|   |   |   |   |   |   | 1 |
| 2 | 3 | 4 | 5 | 6 | 7 | 8 |
| 9 | 10 | 11 | 12 | 13 | 14 | 15 |
| 16 | 17 | 18 | 19 | 20 | 21 | 22 |
| 23 | 24 | 25 | 26 | 27 | 28 | 29 |
| 30 | 31 |   |   |   |   |   |

## NOVEMBER

| M | T | W | T | F | S | S |
|---|---|---|---|---|---|---|
|   |   | 1 | 2 | 3 | 4 | 5 |
| 6 | 7 | 8 | 9 | 10 | 11 | 12 |
| 13 | 14 | 15 | 16 | 17 | 18 | 19 |
| 20 | 21 | 22 | 23 | 24 | 25 | 26 |
| 27 | 28 | 29 | 30 |   |   |   |

## DECEMBER

| M | T | W | T | F | S | S |
|---|---|---|---|---|---|---|
|   |   |   |   | 1 | 2 | 3 |
| 4 | 5 | 6 | 7 | 8 | 9 | 10 |
| 11 | 12 | 13 | 14 | 15 | 16 | 17 |
| 18 | 19 | 20 | 21 | 22 | 23 | 24 |
| 25 | 26 | 27 | 28 | 29 | 30 | 31 |

7 August 2023, Monday, August Bank Holiday
30 October 2023, Monday, October Bank Holiday

25 December 2023, Monday, Christmas Day
26 December 2023, Tuesday, St Stephen's Day

# 2023 GOALS

# 2023 GOALS

_____

_____

_____

_____

_____

_____

_____

_____

_____

_____

_____

_____

_____

_____

_____

_____

_____

_____

_____

_____

_____

_____

_____

_____

Keep track of all your plans and how many precious annual leave days you have left.

Annual leave
23rd Jan – 1 DAy.

# HOLIDAY PLANNER

**Birthstone: garnet**

**Flowers: carnation and snowdrop**

PERSONALITY TRAITS

You're calm, optimistic and, as
Mammy says about Majella, you
march to the beat of your own drum.

# January

| MONDAY | TUESDAY | WEDNESDAY |
|--------|---------|-----------|
| 26 | 27 | 28 |
| 2 | 3 | 4 |
| 9 | 10 | 11 |
| 16 | 17 | 18 |
| 23 | 24 | 25 |
| 30 | 31 | 1 |

| THURSDAY | FRIDAY | SATURDAY | SUNDAY |
|---|---|---|---|
| 29 | 30 | 31 | 1 |
| 5 | 6 | 7 | 8 |
| 12 | 13 | 14 | 15 |
| 19 | 20 | 21 | 22 |
| 26 | 27 | 28 | 29 |
| 2 | 3 | 4 | 5 |

# AISLING'S DIARY

I've often wondered if it's possible to actually die of embarrassment and, diary, today I got my answer. After a winter growth spurt Mammy looked me up and down and declared that I needed a bra. Finally! Goodbye cropped vest! I was hoping she'd bring me to Penneys – Majella got a pink one there that she can pack a shocking amount of toilet roll into – but, before I knew it, the Avensis was pulling up outside bloody Geraldine's Boutique.

As soon as I spotted a group of Knock Rangers minors eating chips on the little stone wall outside, I begged her to bring me somewhere funkier. But she said I'll need something with decent support in a few months if her own bust is anything to go by and that Geraldine carries a great selection of Playtex. No chance of anything with padding for me so.

She was out of the car like a shot absolutely oblivious to the fact that I was going to have to walk past all those hurlers by myself. I took a deep breath and examined the cuffs of my school jumper while she marched ahead, rooting in her handbag. She pushed the door of Geraldine's, triggering the bell. Of course this made all the lads look up at once.

'Hurry up, Aisling,' she called back at me. 'I can already tell you're a 32AA, but we'll get Geraldine to measure you anyway.'

# ALL ABOUT JANUARY

## GOALS FOR JANUARY

_____
_____
_____
_____
_____
_____
_____
_____
_____
_____
_____
_____

## NEW THINGS TO READ/ WATCH/MAKE/EAT

_____
_____
_____
_____
_____
_____
_____
_____
_____
_____
_____

## MUST GET DONE

_____
_____
_____
_____
_____
_____
_____
_____
_____
_____
_____
_____

## SELF-CARE IDEAS

_____
_____
_____
_____
_____
_____
_____
_____
_____
_____
_____
_____

26 MONDAY DECEMBER

27 TUESDAY

28 WEDNESDAY

29 THURSDAY

30 FRIDAY

31 SATURDAY NEW YEAR'S EVE

1 **SUNDAY JANUARY**
NEW YEAR'S DAY

IMPORTANT BITS

| M | T | W | T | F | S | S |
|----|----|----|----|----|----|----|
| | | | | | | 1 |
| 2 | 3 | 4 | 5 | 6 | 7 | 8 |
| 9 | 10 | 11 | 12 | 13 | 14 | 15 |
| 16 | 17 | 18 | 19 | 20 | 21 | 22 |
| 23 | 24 | 25 | 26 | 27 | 28 | 29 |
| 30 | 31 | | | | | |

## JANUARY 2-8

2 MONDAY

3 TUESDAY

4 WEDNESDAY

5 THURSDAY

6 FRIDAY

7 SATURDAY

8 SUNDAY

IMPORTANT BITS

| M | T | W | T | F | S | S |
|---|---|---|---|---|---|---|
|   |   |   |   |   |   | 1 |
| 2 | 3 | 4 | 5 | 6 | 7 | 8 |
| 9 | 10 | 11 | 12 | 13 | 14 | 15 |
| 16 | 17 | 18 | 19 | 20 | 21 | 22 |
| 23 | 24 | 25 | 26 | 27 | 28 | 29 |
| 30 | 31 |   |   |   |   |   |

9 MONDAY

10 TUESDAY

11 WEDNESDAY

12 THURSDAY

13 FRIDAY

## 14 SATURDAY

## 15 SUNDAY

---

## IMPORTANT BITS

| M | T | W | T | F | S | S |
|---|---|---|---|---|---|---|
|   |   |   |   |   |   | 1 |
| 2 | 3 | 4 | 5 | 6 | 7 | 8 |
| 9 | 10 | 11 | 12 | 13 | 14 | 15 |
| 16 | 17 | 18 | 19 | 20 | 21 | 22 |
| 23 | 24 | 25 | 26 | 27 | 28 | 29 |
| 30 | 31 |   |   |   |   |   |

16 MONDAY

17 TUESDAY

18 WEDNESDAY

19 THURSDAY

20 FRIDAY

## 21 SATURDAY

## 22 SUNDAY

IMPORTANT BITS

| M | T | W | T | F | S | S |
|---|---|---|---|---|---|---|
| | | | | | | 1 |
| 2 | 3 | 4 | 5 | 6 | 7 | 8 |
| 9 | 10 | 11 | 12 | 13 | 14 | 15 |
| 16 | 17 | 18 | 19 | 20 | 21 | 22 |
| 23 | 24 | 25 | 26 | 27 | 28 | 29 |
| 30 | 31 | | | | | |

23 MONDAY

24 TUESDAY

25 WEDNESDAY

26 THURSDAY AUSTRALIA DAY

27 FRIDAY

28 SATURDAY

29 SUNDAY

IMPORTANT BITS

| M | T | W | T | F | S | S |
|---|---|---|---|---|---|---|
|   |   |   |   |   |   | 1 |
| 2 | 3 | 4 | 5 | 6 | 7 | 8 |
| 9 | 10 | 11 | 12 | 13 | 14 | 15 |
| 16 | 17 | 18 | 19 | 20 | 21 | 22 |
| 23 | 24 | 25 | 26 | 27 | 28 | 29 |
| 30 | 31 |   |   |   |   |   |

3 0 MONDAY

3 1 TUESDAY

1 WEDNESDAY FEBRUARY

2 THURSDAY

3 FRIDAY

4 SATURDAY

5 SUNDAY

IMPORTANT BITS

| M | T | W | T | F | S | S |
|---|---|---|---|---|---|---|
| | | | | | | 1 |
| 2 | 3 | 4 | 5 | 6 | 7 | 8 |
| 9 | 10 | 11 | 12 | 13 | 14 | 15 |
| 16 | 17 | 18 | 19 | 20 | 21 | 22 |
| 23 | 24 | 25 | 26 | 27 | 28 | 29 |
| 30 | 31 | | | | | |

# JANUARY NOTES

Birthstone: amethyst

Flowers: violet, iris and primrose

## PERSONALITY TRAITS

February babies are unique,
creative and generous. This
makes for a perfect Rose of
Tralee if you're feeling ambitious.

February

| MONDAY | TUESDAY | WEDNESDAY |
|--------|---------|-----------|
| 30 | 31 | 1 |
| 6 | 7 | 8 |
| 13 | 14 | 15 |
| 20 | 21 | 22 |
| 27 | 28 | 1 |
| 6 | 7 | 8 |

| THURSDAY | FRIDAY | SATURDAY | SUNDAY |
|---|---|---|---|
| 2 | 3 | 4 | 5 |
| 9 | 10 | 11 | 12 |
| 16 | 17 | 18 | 19 |
| 23 | 24 | 25 | 26 |
| 2 | 3 | 4 | 5 |
| 9 | 10 | 11 | 12 |

# AISLING'S DIARY

Oh my God, oh my God, oh my God, I hope I go to sleep tonight and wake up in ten years' time because I have never been so mortified. First of all, Mammy went into my schoolbag this morning and found the Valentine's card I got for Colm McGonagle and took it out in front of Daddy and Paul. She said she was only giving me a mandarin for my little break, but I know she was rooting. Daddy nearly put his whole face into his Weetabix, but Paul laughed so much Mammy had to get out the nebuliser.

It might not have been so bad only the card was as big as my geography book and had a huge padded heart on it. The dearest one they had in Filan's! I had to hide it behind a box of Donegal Catch when I was buying it. I considered wearing a disguise but all I had was my skeleton mask from two Halloweens ago.

Majella swore blind she was going to get the same card for Seán Ó Súilleabháin and we could give them to the lads together after school but then she chickened out and gave him a Golden Crisp instead. Colm took one look at the card I gave him and said, 'Why did you get me that?' Then he shoved the smallest card in the world at me and I didn't even get the kiss on the lips I had been gearing myself up for all day. Majella's already kissed Seán on the lips six times and one time felt his tongue, she thinks.

When I got home Mammy went all sappy asking me did my Valentine like his card. I slammed the door and she called me a little rip. Love is cursed. I'm going to be a nun.

# ALL ABOUT FEBRUARY

## GOALS FOR
## FEBRUARY

_____

_____

_____

_____

_____

_____

_____

_____

_____

_____

_____

## NEW THINGS TO READ/
## WATCH/MAKE/EAT

_____

_____

_____

_____

_____

_____

_____

_____

_____

_____

_____

## MUST GET DONE

_____

_____

_____

_____

_____

_____

_____

_____

_____

_____

_____

## SELF-CARE IDEAS

_____

_____

_____

_____

_____

_____

_____

_____

_____

_____

_____

30 MONDAY JANUARY

31 TUESDAY

1 WEDNESDAY FEBRUARY ST BRIGID'S DAY

2 THURSDAY

3 FRIDAY

4 SATURDAY

5 SUNDAY

IMPORTANT BITS

| M | T | W | T | F | S | S |
|---|---|---|---|---|---|---|
| | | 1 | 2 | 3 | 4 | 5 |
| 6 | 7 | 8 | 9 | 10 | 11 | 12 |
| 13 | 14 | 15 | 16 | 17 | 18 | 19 |
| 20 | 21 | 22 | 23 | 24 | 25 | 26 |
| 27 | 28 | | | | | |

6 **MONDAY** FEBRUARY BANK HOLIDAY

7 TUESDAY

8 WEDNESDAY

9 THURSDAY

10 FRIDAY

## 11 SATURDAY

## 12 SUNDAY

IMPORTANT BITS

| M | T | W | T | F | S | S |
|---|---|---|---|---|---|---|
|   |   | 1 | 2 | 3 | 4 | 5 |
| 6 | 7 | 8 | 9 | 10 | 11 | 12 |
| 13 | 14 | 15 | 16 | 17 | 18 | 19 |
| 20 | 21 | 22 | 23 | 24 | 25 | 26 |
| 27 | 28 |   |   |   |   |   |

13 MONDAY

14 TUESDAY VALENTINE'S DAY

15 WEDNESDAY

16 THURSDAY

17 FRIDAY

# 18 SATURDAY

# 19 SUNDAY

## IMPORTANT BITS

| M | T | W | T | F | S | S |
|---|---|---|---|---|---|---|
|   |   | 1 | 2 | 3 | 4 | 5 |
| 6 | 7 | 8 | 9 | 10 | 11 | 12 |
| 13 | 14 | 15 | 16 | 17 | 18 | 19 |
| 20 | 21 | 22 | 23 | 24 | 25 | 26 |
| 27 | 28 |   |   |   |   |   |

20 MONDAY

21 **TUESDAY** PANCAKE TUESDAY

22 WEDNESDAY

23 THURSDAY

24 FRIDAY

25 SATURDAY

26 SUNDAY

IMPORTANT BITS

| M | T | W | T | F | S | S |
|---|---|---|---|---|---|---|
|  |  | 1 | 2 | 3 | 4 | 5 |
| 6 | 7 | 8 | 9 | 10 | 11 | 12 |
| 13 | 14 | 15 | 16 | 17 | 18 | 19 |
| 20 | 21 | 22 | 23 | 24 | 25 | 26 |
| 27 | 28 |  |  |  |  |  |

27 MONDAY

28 TUESDAY

1 WEDNESDAY MARCH

2 THURSDAY

3 FRIDAY

4 SATURDAY

5 SUNDAY

IMPORTANT BITS

| M | T | W | T | F | S | S |
|---|---|---|---|---|---|---|
|   |   | 1 | 2 | 3 | 4 | 5 |
| 6 | 7 | 8 | 9 | 10 | 11 | 12 |
| 13 | 14 | 15 | 16 | 17 | 18 | 19 |
| 20 | 21 | 22 | 23 | 24 | 25 | 26 |
| 27 | 28 |   |   |   |   |   |

Birthstone: aquamarine

Flower: daffodil

## PERSONALITY TRAITS

The daffodil represents rebirth and
new beginnings, which is lovely,
but people born in March are also
as mad as the eponymous hare.
Case in point: Majella.

# March

| MONDAY | TUESDAY | WEDNESDAY |
|--------|---------|-----------|
| 27 | 28 | 1 |
| 6 | 7 | 8 |
| 13 | 14 | 15 |
| 20 | 21 | 22 |
| 27 | 28 | 29 |
| 3 | 4 | 5 |

| THURSDAY | FRIDAY | SATURDAY | SUNDAY |
|---|---|---|---|
| 2 | 3 | 4 | 5 |
| 9 | 10 | 11 | 12 |
| 16 | 17 | 18 | 19 |
| 23 | 24 | 25 | 26 |
| 30 | 31 | 1 | 2 |
| 6 | 7 | 8 | 9 |

# AISLING'S DIARY

I was as surprised as anyone when Sinéad Cloghessy said her cousin Cormac was coming to Ballygobbard for the St Patrick's Day parade tomorrow and wanted to shift me in the handball alley after. The name didn't ring a bell. I thought he might have seen me playing Rolf in our school production of *The Sound of Music* and fallen in love on the spot but when I asked Sinéad she shook her head and turned bright red. Then Majella told me I was the last 'frigit' left in the group and that I was being too fussy. It's not my fault I have high standards!

Sinéad admitted that Cormac didn't even ask for me, that he'd basically shift anything with a pulse.

It's not exactly the romantic proposal I was hoping for but they're right. My first shift – or the prospect of it – has been weighing heavily on me ever since Maeve Hennessey set the ball rolling by getting off with a scout from Cork who was camping on the school grounds last summer. She says she still thinks of him when she smells mildew.

The panic about tomorrow quickly set in and I knew Sinéad could sense it.

'He's not going to want to ...?' I glanced down at the crotch of my O'Neill's. She shook her head.

'God no. Up the top, that's it. I can tell him to stay out of the bra altogether if you want.'

I nodded gratefully. 'That'd be great, thanks.'

I've bought two packets of Extra chewing gum (blue and green) and am going to practise my technique on the back of my wardrobe door tonight. Wish me luck, diary!

# ALL ABOUT MARCH

### GOALS FOR
### MARCH

### NEW THINGS TO READ/
### WATCH/MAKE/EAT

_____

_____

### MUST GET DONE

### SELF-CARE IDEAS

27 MONDAY FEBRUARY

28 TUESDAY

1 WEDNESDAY MARCH

2 THURSDAY

3 FRIDAY

# MARCH

## 4 SATURDAY

## 5 SUNDAY

IMPORTANT BITS

| M | T | W | T | F | S | S |
|---|---|---|---|---|---|---|
| | | 1 | 2 | 3 | 4 | 5 |
| 6 | 7 | 8 | 9 | 10 | 11 | 12 |
| 13 | 14 | 15 | 16 | 17 | 18 | 19 |
| 20 | 21 | 22 | 23 | 24 | 25 | 26 |
| 27 | 28 | 29 | 30 | 31 | | |

6 MONDAY

7 TUESDAY

8 WEDNESDAY INTERNATIONAL WOMEN'S DAY

9 THURSDAY

10 FRIDAY

# 11 SATURDAY

# 12 SUNDAY

## IMPORTANT BITS

| M | T | W | T | F | S | S |
|---|---|---|---|---|---|---|
|  |  | 1 | 2 | 3 | 4 | 5 |
| 6 | 7 | 8 | 9 | 10 | 11 | 12 |
| 13 | 14 | 15 | 16 | 17 | 18 | 19 |
| 20 | 21 | 22 | 23 | 24 | 25 | 26 |
| 27 | 28 | 29 | 30 | 31 |  |  |

13 MONDAY

14 TUESDAY

15 WEDNESDAY

16 THURSDAY

17 FRIDAY ST PATRICK'S DAY

# 18 SATURDAY

# 19 SUNDAY MOTHER'S DAY

## IMPORTANT BITS

| M | T | W | T | F | S | S |
|---|---|---|---|---|---|---|
|   |   | 1 | 2 | 3 | 4 | 5 |
| 6 | 7 | 8 | 9 | 10 | 11 | 12 |
| 13 | 14 | 15 | 16 | 17 | 18 | 19 |
| 20 | 21 | 22 | 23 | 24 | 25 | 26 |
| 27 | 28 | 29 | 30 | 31 |   |   |

20 MONDAY

21 TUESDAY

22 WEDNESDAY

23 THURSDAY

24 FRIDAY

## 25 SATURDAY

## 26 SUNDAY

IMPORTANT BITS

| M | T | W | T | F | S | S |
|---|---|---|---|---|---|---|
|   |   | 1 | 2 | 3 | 4 | 5 |
| 6 | 7 | 8 | 9 | 10 | 11 | 12 |
| 13 | 14 | 15 | 16 | 17 | 18 | 19 |
| 20 | 21 | 22 | 23 | 24 | 25 | 26 |
| 27 | 28 | 29 | 30 | 31 |   |   |

27 MONDAY

28 TUESDAY

29 WEDNESDAY

30 THURSDAY

31 FRIDAY

# MARCH

## 1 SATURDAY APRIL

## 2 SUNDAY

IMPORTANT BITS

| M | T | W | T | F | S | S |
|----|----|----|----|----|----|----|
|    |    | 1  | 2  | 3  | 4  | 5  |
| 6  | 7  | 8  | 9  | 10 | 11 | 12 |
| 13 | 14 | 15 | 16 | 17 | 18 | 19 |
| 20 | 21 | 22 | 23 | 24 | 25 | 26 |
| 27 | 28 | 29 | 30 | 31 |    |    |

**Birthstone: diamond**

**Flowers: daisy and sweet pea**

PERSONALITY TRAITS

You're sensitive, assertive, confident
and most importantly share a birthday
month with Saoirse Ronan, which
brings peace to your heart.

April

| MONDAY | TUESDAY | WEDNESDAY |
|--------|---------|-----------|
| 27 | 28 | 29 |
| 3 | 4 | 5 |
| 10 | 11 | 12 |
| 17 | 18 | 19 |
| 24 | 25 | 26 |
| 1 | 2 | 3 |

| THURSDAY | FRIDAY | SATURDAY | SUNDAY |
|----------|--------|----------|--------|
| 30 | 31 | 1 | 2 |
| 6 | 7 | 8 | 9 |
| 13 | 14 | 15 | 16 |
| 20 | 21 | 22 | 23 |
| 27 | 28 | 29 | 30 |
| 4 | 5 | 6 | 7 |

# AISLING'S DIARY

Well, I'm glad I brought my diary with me so I can document every detail of this palace I'm in. My usual babysitting gig is for the Hynes triplets and they're a nightmare ever since they were on Ireland AM documenting their first day of school. They didn't lick it off a stone, because Maura Hynes has copies of it on video and all of their newspaper cuttings framed in the sitting room. Mark my words they'll be legally emancipated like Macaulay Culkin by the time they're fifteen.

I'm not at Hynes's tonight though. Niamh from Across the Road (posho) had to bring her pony (puke!) to a gymkhana (excuuuse me!) in Kildare, so I've stepped in to babysit her usual gang in the Big House out on the Knocknamanagh Road. I always thought she was just being a sickener boasting about the size of the telly and the quality of the snacks, but I did a kitchen sweep the second the lights of the Range Rover were safely out of the driveway and all signs point towards this lot doing their Big Shop in Marks & Spencer. It's nearly an hour to the nearest one. That's dedication to the notions.

The baby woke up once already, but I just crawled in and shoved the dodie back in his mouth, rolled back out again and he seems grand. The little girl hasn't made a sound. Sure, why would you wake up crying when you've this much money? Niamh said they pay twenty quid an hour and I've my eye on the Britney Spears Skechers. Praying for at least a 2 a.m. return.

# ALL ABOUT APRIL

## GOALS FOR APRIL

_____
_____
_____
_____
_____
_____
_____
_____
_____
_____
_____

## NEW THINGS TO READ/ WATCH/MAKE/EAT

_____
_____
_____
_____
_____
_____
_____
_____
_____
_____
_____

## MUST GET DONE

_____
_____
_____
_____
_____
_____
_____
_____
_____
_____

## SELF-CARE IDEAS

_____
_____
_____
_____
_____
_____
_____
_____
_____
_____

27 MONDAY MARCH

28 TUESDAY

29 WEDNESDAY

30 THURSDAY

31 FRIDAY

## 1 SATURDAY APRIL

## 2 SUNDAY

### IMPORTANT BITS

| M | T | W | T | F | S | S |
|---|---|---|---|---|---|---|
| | | | | | 1 | 2 |
| 3 | 4 | 5 | 6 | 7 | 8 | 9 |
| 10 | 11 | 12 | 13 | 14 | 15 | 16 |
| 17 | 18 | 19 | 20 | 21 | 22 | 23 |
| 24 | 25 | 26 | 27 | 28 | 29 | 30 |

3 MONDAY

4 TUESDAY

5 WEDNESDAY

6 THURSDAY

7 FRIDAY GOOD FRIDAY

8 SATURDAY

9 SUNDAY EASTER SUNDAY

IMPORTANT BITS

| M | T | W | T | F | S | S |
|---|---|---|---|---|---|---|
| | | | | | 1 | 2 |
| 3 | 4 | 5 | 6 | 7 | 8 | 9 |
| 10 | 11 | 12 | 13 | 14 | 15 | 16 |
| 17 | 18 | 19 | 20 | 21 | 22 | 23 |
| 24 | 25 | 26 | 27 | 28 | 29 | 30 |

10 **MONDAY** EASTER MONDAY

11 TUESDAY

12 WEDNESDAY

13 THURSDAY

14 FRIDAY

15 SATURDAY

16 SUNDAY

IMPORTANT BITS

| M | T | W | T | F | S | S |
|---|---|---|---|---|---|---|
|   |   |   |   |   | 1 | 2 |
| 3 | 4 | 5 | 6 | 7 | 8 | 9 |
| 10 | 11 | 12 | 13 | 14 | 15 | 16 |
| 17 | 18 | 19 | 20 | 21 | 22 | 23 |
| 24 | 25 | 26 | 27 | 28 | 29 | 30 |

17 MONDAY

18 TUESDAY

19 WEDNESDAY

20 THURSDAY

21 FRIDAY

22 SATURDAY

23 SUNDAY

IMPORTANT BITS

| M | T | W | T | F | S | S |
|---|---|---|---|---|---|---|
|  |  |  |  |  | 1 | 2 |
| 3 | 4 | 5 | 6 | 7 | 8 | 9 |
| 10 | 11 | 12 | 13 | 14 | 15 | 16 |
| 17 | 18 | 19 | 20 | 21 | 22 | 23 |
| 24 | 25 | 26 | 27 | 28 | 29 | 30 |

24 MONDAY

25 TUESDAY

26 WEDNESDAY

27 THURSDAY

28 FRIDAY

## 29 SATURDAY

## 30 SUNDAY

IMPORTANT BITS

| M | T | W | T | F | S | S |
|---|---|---|---|---|---|---|
| | | | | | 1 | 2 |
| 3 | 4 | 5 | 6 | 7 | 8 | 9 |
| 10 | 11 | 12 | 13 | 14 | 15 | 16 |
| 17 | 18 | 19 | 20 | 21 | 22 | 23 |
| 24 | 25 | 26 | 27 | 28 | 29 | 30 |

Birthstone: emerald

Flower: lily of the valley

## PERSONALITY TRAITS

Mary might be queen of the angels and queen of the month of May, but you're queen of having a positive attitude and excellent career potential.

May

| MONDAY | TUESDAY | WEDNESDAY |
|--------|---------|-----------|
| 24 | 25 | 26 |
| 1 | 2 | 3 |
| 8 | 9 | 10 |
| 15 | 16 | 17 |
| 22 | 23 | 24 |
| 29 | 30 | 31 |

| THURSDAY | FRIDAY | SATURDAY | SUNDAY |
|----------|--------|----------|--------|
| 27 | 28 | 29 | 30 |
| 4 | 5 | 6 | 7 |
| 11 | 12 | 13 | 14 |
| 18 | 19 | 20 | 21 |
| 25 | 26 | 27 | 28 |
| 1 | 2 | 3 | 4 |

**2 MAY 2004, AGE 15**

Diary, I finally did it. And I'm alive to tell the tale.

I've been thinking about it and talking myself in and out of it for months now. I even asked Fr Fenlon his opinion in the confession box last Saturday, but he was no use. In fact he kicked me out and told me to say seven Hail Marys for wasting clerical time! I wouldn't mind but there was only Mad Tom after me in the queue, although he does seem to have a lot to say once he gets inside. Daddy reckons it's because of all the cow tipping.

I had originally decided to use the element of surprise and tell Mammy during the first break in *Desperate Housewives*. That gardener tends to put her in a good mood, plus an ad break is only three minutes long and realistically what can she do to me in three minutes? But Paul talked me out of it, asking why I would tell Mammy when I could just tell Daddy, seeing as I'm clearly his pet?

I know it was a dig but he's right of course. It's not that it's even a big deal – at least three other girls in my class have done it and the world hasn't ended. I waited until he'd eaten his chops and Mammy had just left for Aqua Aerobics with Úna Hatton. After I choked out the words, he just sighed, said, 'Your mother will hit the roof,' and went back to his apple tart and copy of the *Farmers Journal*.

I was perfecting my cross-section diagram of the Earth's crust for geography when I heard the back door close. Not forty seconds later my bedroom door burst open and there she was: Mammy. Livid. 'What do you mean you're dropping down to Pass Maths?' she roared so loudly that my framed picture of Shane Filan fell off the windowsill. At least it's done now.

# ALL ABOUT MAY

### GOALS FOR
### MAY

_____

_____

_____

_____

_____

_____

_____

_____

_____

_____

### NEW THINGS TO READ/
### WATCH/MAKE/EAT

_____

_____

_____

_____

_____

_____

_____

_____

_____

_____

### MUST GET DONE

_____

_____

_____

_____

_____

_____

_____

_____

_____

_____

### SELF-CARE IDEAS

_____

_____

_____

_____

_____

_____

_____

_____

_____

_____

1 MONDAY MAY DAY

2 TUESDAY

3 WEDNESDAY

4 THURSDAY

5 FRIDAY

6 SATURDAY

7 SUNDAY

IMPORTANT BITS

| M | T | W | T | F | S | S |
|---|---|---|---|---|---|---|
| 1 | 2 | 3 | 4 | 5 | 6 | 7 |
| 8 | 9 | 10 | 11 | 12 | 13 | 14 |
| 15 | 16 | 17 | 18 | 19 | 20 | 21 |
| 22 | 23 | 24 | 25 | 26 | 27 | 28 |
| 29 | 30 | 31 | | | | |

8 MONDAY

9 TUESDAY

10 WEDNESDAY

11 THURSDAY

12 FRIDAY

# 13 SATURDAY

# 14 SUNDAY

## IMPORTANT BITS

| M | T | W | T | F | S | S |
|---|---|---|---|---|---|---|
| 1 | 2 | 3 | 4 | 5 | 6 | 7 |
| 8 | 9 | 10 | 11 | 12 | 13 | 14 |
| 15 | 16 | 17 | 18 | 19 | 20 | 21 |
| 22 | 23 | 24 | 25 | 26 | 27 | 28 |
| 29 | 30 | 31 | | | | |

15 MONDAY

16 TUESDAY

17 WEDNESDAY

18 THURSDAY

19 FRIDAY

20 <sup>SATURDAY</sup>

21 <sup>SUNDAY</sup>

IMPORTANT BITS

| M | T | W | T | F | S | S |
|---|---|---|---|---|---|---|
| 1 | 2 | 3 | 4 | 5 | 6 | 7 |
| 8 | 9 | 10 | 11 | 12 | 13 | 14 |
| 15 | 16 | 17 | 18 | 19 | 20 | 21 |
| 22 | 23 | 24 | 25 | 26 | 27 | 28 |
| 29 | 30 | 31 | | | | |

MAY 22–28

22 MONDAY

23 TUESDAY

24 WEDNESDAY

25 THURSDAY

26 FRIDAY

## 27 SATURDAY

## 28 SUNDAY

IMPORTANT BITS

| M | T | W | T | F | S | S |
|---|---|---|---|---|---|---|
| 1 | 2 | 3 | 4 | 5 | 6 | 7 |
| 8 | 9 | 10 | 11 | 12 | 13 | 14 |
| 15 | 16 | 17 | 18 | 19 | 20 | 21 |
| 22 | 23 | 24 | 25 | 26 | 27 | 28 |
| 29 | 30 | 31 | | | | |

29 MONDAY

30 TUESDAY

31 WEDNESDAY

1 THURSDAY JUNE

2 FRIDAY

3 SATURDAY

4 SUNDAY

IMPORTANT BITS

| M | T | W | T | F | S | S |
|---|---|---|---|---|---|---|
| 1 | 2 | 3 | 4 | 5 | 6 | 7 |
| 8 | 9 | 10 | 11 | 12 | 13 | 14 |
| 15 | 16 | 17 | 18 | 19 | 20 | 21 |
| 22 | 23 | 24 | 25 | 26 | 27 | 28 |
| 29 | 30 | 31 | | | | |

Birthstone: pearl

Flowers: rose and honeysuckle

## PERSONALITY TRAITS

People born in June are
optimistic, cheerful and tend to
believe that a good Irish summer
is on the way, God love them.

# June

| MONDAY | TUESDAY | WEDNESDAY |
|--------|---------|-----------|
| 29 | 30 | 31 |
| 5 | 6 | 7 |
| 12 | 13 | 14 |
| 19 | 20 | 21 |
| 26 | 27 | 28 |
| 3 | 4 | 5 |

| THURSDAY | FRIDAY | SATURDAY | SUNDAY |
|----------|--------|----------|--------|
| 1 | 2 | 3 | 4 |
| 8 | 9 | 10 | 11 |
| 15 | 16 | 17 | 18 |
| 22 | 23 | 24 | 25 |
| 29 | 30 | 1 | 2 |
| 6 | 7 | 8 | 9 |

# AISLING'S DIARY

**16 JUNE 2004, AGE 15, 8.15 A.M.**

*Es freut mich!* I can't believe this day is here. One more Junior Cert exam and then we're free! I feel fairly good about my German tape and learned off one letter home from my holidays and one email about growing up on a farm. No matter what happens I'm getting the German words for sheep dip and baling twine in there somewhere after going to the trouble of learning them. Majella has a free gaff later so we're going to her house and Sinéad Cloghessy's brother is getting us drink from Filan's. I hope it's not just beer because I tasted Kaliber at Deirdre Ruane's brother's confirmation, and it was terrible tack. We were falling around drunk in the back garden until Majella noticed that there was no alcohol in it. Tonight though, we're getting locked! First time ever!

**17 JUNE 2004, AGE 15, 11 A.M.**

I'm never drinking again. I don't know how I managed to get past Daddy and up the stairs and him trying to talk to me about entering calves into the Pride of BGB talent competition. If I die, three bottles of Smirnoff Ice and a vodka and Coke are what killed me. I got sick in Majella's mother's Christmas pudding bowl. Majella got sick into her own pillowcase. Deirdre Ruane fell over the dog, and he bit her on the thigh, but she was two Bacardi Breezers in and didn't feel a thing. I'll never be able to drink Coke again and I'll have to stay up here all day and say I have food poisoning.

At least My Summer Holidays came up on the German exam. I got in four mentions of baling twine.

# ALL ABOUT JUNE

## GOALS FOR JUNE

_____
_____
_____
_____
_____
_____
_____
_____
_____
_____
_____

## NEW THINGS TO READ/ WATCH/MAKE/EAT

_____
_____
_____
_____
_____
_____
_____
_____
_____
_____

## MUST GET DONE

_____
_____
_____
_____
_____
_____
_____
_____
_____
_____

## SELF-CARE IDEAS

_____
_____
_____
_____
_____
_____
_____
_____
_____
_____

29 MONDAY MAY

30 TUESDAY

31 WEDNESDAY

1 THURSDAY JUNE

2 FRIDAY

3 SATURDAY

4 SUNDAY

IMPORTANT BITS

| M | T | W | T | F | S | S |
|----|----|----|----|----|----|----|
|    |    |    | 1  | 2  | 3  | 4  |
| 5  | 6  | 7  | 8  | 9  | 10 | 11 |
| 12 | 13 | 14 | 15 | 16 | 17 | 18 |
| 19 | 20 | 21 | 22 | 23 | 24 | 25 |
| 26 | 27 | 28 | 29 | 30 |    |    |

5 **MONDAY** JUNE BANK HOLIDAY

6 TUESDAY

7 WEDNESDAY

8 THURSDAY

9 FRIDAY

# 10 SATURDAY

# 11 SUNDAY

## IMPORTANT BITS

| M | T | W | T | F | S | S |
|---|---|---|---|---|---|---|
|   |   |   | 1 | 2 | 3 | 4 |
| 5 | 6 | 7 | 8 | 9 | 10 | 11 |
| 12 | 13 | 14 | 15 | 16 | 17 | 18 |
| 19 | 20 | 21 | 22 | 23 | 24 | 25 |
| 26 | 27 | 28 | 29 | 30 |   |   |

12 MONDAY

13 TUESDAY

14 WEDNESDAY

15 THURSDAY NADINE COYLE'S BIRTHDAY

16 FRIDAY

# 17 SATURDAY

# 18 SUNDAY FATHER'S DAY

IMPORTANT BITS

| M | T | W | T | F | S | S |
|---|---|---|---|---|---|---|
|   |   |   | 1 | 2 | 3 | 4 |
| 5 | 6 | 7 | 8 | 9 | 10 | 11 |
| 12 | 13 | 14 | 15 | 16 | 17 | 18 |
| 19 | 20 | 21 | 22 | 23 | 24 | 25 |
| 26 | 27 | 28 | 29 | 30 |   |   |

19 MONDAY

20 TUESDAY

21 WEDNESDAY

22 THURSDAY

23 FRIDAY

## 24 SATURDAY

## 25 SUNDAY

IMPORTANT BITS

| M | T | W | T | F | S | S |
|---|---|---|---|---|---|---|
|   |   |   | 1 | 2 | 3 | 4 |
| 5 | 6 | 7 | 8 | 9 | 10 | 11 |
| 12 | 13 | 14 | 15 | 16 | 17 | 18 |
| 19 | 20 | 21 | 22 | 23 | 24 | 25 |
| 26 | 27 | 28 | 29 | 30 |   |   |

26 MONDAY

27 TUESDAY

28 WEDNESDAY

29 THURSDAY

30 FRIDAY

# JUNE

1 SATURDAY JULY

2 SUNDAY

IMPORTANT BITS

| M | T | W | T | F | S | S |
|---|---|---|---|---|---|---|
| | | | 1 | 2 | 3 | 4 |
| 5 | 6 | 7 | 8 | 9 | 10 | 11 |
| 12 | 13 | 14 | 15 | 16 | 17 | 18 |
| 19 | 20 | 21 | 22 | 23 | 24 | 25 |
| 26 | 27 | 28 | 29 | 30 | | |

# JUNE NOTES

Birthstone: ruby

Flowers: larkspur, tulip and waterlily

## PERSONALITY TRAITS

July babies are curious about learning new things and have an amazing sense of humour, which they've been forced to cultivate after years of not having a birthday party at school.

July

| MONDAY | TUESDAY | WEDNESDAY |
|--------|---------|-----------|
| 26 | 27 | 28 |
| 3 | 4 | 5 |
| 10 | 11 | 12 |
| 17 | 18 | 19 |
| 24 | 25 | 26 |
| 31 | 1 | 2 |

JULY AT A GLANCE

| THURSDAY | FRIDAY | SATURDAY | SUNDAY |
|---|---|---|---|
| 29 | 30 | 1 | 2 |
| 6 | 7 | 8 | 9 |
| 13 | 14 | 15 | 16 |
| 20 | 21 | 22 | 23 |
| 27 | 28 | 29 | 30 |
| 3 | 4 | 5 | 6 |

**28 JULY 2005, AGED 16**

Well, I don't think I'll be coming back from Donegal fluent in Irish after all, although it's not for the want of trying.

Since we finished dinner – *dinnéar* – an hour ago, there's been nothing but *Béarla* spoken in the room I'm sharing with Majella and eight girls from South Dublin who brought three suitcases each. They were really putting us to shame with the style until Maj ingratiated herself with one of them during a dispute with the *bean an tí* over pepperoni pizza not being vegetarian. I can't fault Máire's cooking but she runs a very tight ship, in every sense of the word.

Long story short, me and Maj now have access to more swish make-up, clothes from Topshop and statement necklaces than we know what to do with, as well as a GHD hair straightener. I really did intend on leaving here knowing my *tuiseal ginideach* inside out, but I can't get a word in edgeways since the news broke over dessert – *milseog* – that there's going to be a themed *ceilí* every evening.

Tomorrow each house has to perform a sort of party piece in front of the whole college. The pressure! I suggested translating a song into Irish and coming up with a dance to go with it and Simone and the girls thought it was a class idea. After I ring home to say goodnight to the cat, I have to get started on the song, as chosen by Majella. She says if we get the moves right we might even make it onto the news!

# ALL ABOUT JULY

## GOALS FOR JULY

_____
_____
_____
_____
_____
_____
_____
_____
_____
_____
_____

## NEW THINGS TO READ/ WATCH/MAKE/EAT

_____
_____
_____
_____
_____
_____
_____
_____
_____
_____
_____

## MUST GET DONE

_____
_____
_____
_____
_____
_____
_____
_____
_____
_____
_____

## SELF-CARE IDEAS

_____
_____
_____
_____
_____
_____
_____
_____
_____
_____
_____

26 MONDAY JUNE

27 TUESDAY

28 WEDNESDAY

29 THURSDAY

30 FRIDAY

# 1 SATURDAY **JULY** CANADA DAY

# 2 SUNDAY

IMPORTANT BITS

| M | T | W | T | F | S | S |
|---|---|---|---|---|---|---|
| | | | | | 1 | 2 |
| 3 | 4 | 5 | 6 | 7 | 8 | 9 |
| 10 | 11 | 12 | 13 | 14 | 15 | 16 |
| 17 | 18 | 19 | 20 | 21 | 22 | 23 |
| 24 | 25 | 26 | 27 | 28 | 29 | 30 |
| 31 | | | | | | |

3 MONDAY

4 TUESDAY

5 WEDNESDAY

6 THURSDAY

7 FRIDAY

## 8 SATURDAY

## 9 SUNDAY

## IMPORTANT BITS

| M | T | W | T | F | S | S |
|---|---|---|---|---|---|---|
| | | | | | 1 | 2 |
| 3 | 4 | 5 | 6 | 7 | 8 | 9 |
| 10 | 11 | 12 | 13 | 14 | 15 | 16 |
| 17 | 18 | 19 | 20 | 21 | 22 | 23 |
| 24 | 25 | 26 | 27 | 28 | 29 | 30 |
| 31 | | | | | | |

10 MONDAY

11 TUESDAY

12 WEDNESDAY

13 THURSDAY

14 FRIDAY BASTILLE DAY

## 15 SATURDAY

## 16 SUNDAY

IMPORTANT BITS

| M | T | W | T | F | S | S |
|---|---|---|---|---|---|---|
| | | | | | 1 | 2 |
| 3 | 4 | 5 | 6 | 7 | 8 | 9 |
| 10 | 11 | 12 | 13 | 14 | 15 | 16 |
| 17 | 18 | 19 | 20 | 21 | 22 | 23 |
| 24 | 25 | 26 | 27 | 28 | 29 | 30 |
| 31 | | | | | | |

17 MONDAY

18 TUESDAY

19 WEDNESDAY

20 THURSDAY

21 FRIDAY

## 22 SATURDAY

## 23 SUNDAY

IMPORTANT BITS

| M | T | W | T | F | S | S |
|---|---|---|---|---|---|---|
|   |   |   |   |   | 1 | 2 |
| 3 | 4 | 5 | 6 | 7 | 8 | 9 |
| 10 | 11 | 12 | 13 | 14 | 15 | 16 |
| 17 | 18 | 19 | 20 | 21 | 22 | 23 |
| 24 | 25 | 26 | 27 | 28 | 29 | 30 |
| 31 |   |   |   |   |   |   |

24 MONDAY

25 TUESDAY

26 WEDNESDAY

27 THURSDAY

28 FRIDAY

# 29 SATURDAY

# 30 SUNDAY

IMPORTANT BITS

| M | T | W | T | F | S | S |
|---|---|---|---|---|---|---|
| | | | | | 1 | 2 |
| 3 | 4 | 5 | 6 | 7 | 8 | 9 |
| 10 | 11 | 12 | 13 | 14 | 15 | 16 |
| 17 | 18 | 19 | 20 | 21 | 22 | 23 |
| 24 | 25 | 26 | 27 | 28 | 29 | 30 |
| 31 | | | | | | |

31 **MONDAY**

1 TUESDAY AUGUST

2 WEDNESDAY

3 THURSDAY

4 FRIDAY

5 SATURDAY

6 SUNDAY

IMPORTANT BITS

| M | T | W | T | F | S | S |
|----|----|----|----|----|----|----|
|    |    |    |    |    | 1 | 2 |
| 3  | 4  | 5  | 6  | 7  | 8 | 9 |
| 10 | 11 | 12 | 13 | 14 | 15 | 16 |
| 17 | 18 | 19 | 20 | 21 | 22 | 23 |
| 24 | 25 | 26 | 27 | 28 | 29 | 30 |
| 31 |    |    |    |    |    |    |

Birthstone: peridot

Flowers: gladiolus and poppy

## PERSONALITY TRAITS

People born in August wear their
hearts on their sleeves, have fire in
their soul, and a mouth they can't
control. At least that's what the mug in
Claire's Accessories said.

August

AUGUST AT A GLANCE

| MONDAY | TUESDAY | WEDNESDAY |
|--------|---------|-----------|
| 31 | 1 | 2 |
| 7 | 8 | 9 |
| 14 | 15 | 16 |
| 21 | 22 | 23 |
| 28 | 29 | 30 |
| 4 | 5 | 6 |

| THURSDAY | FRIDAY | SATURDAY | SUNDAY |
|----------|--------|----------|--------|
| 3 | 4 | 5 | 6 |
| 10 | 11 | 12 | 13 |
| 17 | 18 | 19 | 20 |
| 24 | 25 | 26 | 27 |
| 31 | 1 | 2 | 3 |
| 7 | 8 | 9 | 10 |

**14 AUGUST 2005, AGE 16**

I've never known power like it. Being at the helm of the Lotto machine and the ice cream machine during a heatwave and a bumper jackpot weekend is what I imagine it's like to run the big slide at a waterpark or do the security at a Garth Brooks ticket counter. Majella said she's worried the power is going to my head after I made two eleven-year-olds go all the way to the back of the ice cream queue because they were dithering over sauce choices. I warned Eamon Filan that introducing a third flavour – caramel – would lead to problems.

Eamon and I have been working together like ballet dancers since the heatwave started – him on the Lotto and me on the 99s and then switching over when we need a break from either machine. I never thought a summer job in Filan's could make me feel like Diane Keaton in *Baby Boom* but I'm only days away from getting a power suit and insisting Eamon turns the storage shed into a corporate meeting room.

The heat means that when we close at eight there's still time to go and jump in the river with Majella. She's working in a creche in Knocknamanagh for the summer. She says she's swearing off children for life but if she wants to be a teacher she's going to have to get used to snotty noses and tantrums over nothing. If I was in the creche I'd have them ship-shape and roar at them like I do over the Quick Picks.

Maybe Majella has a point about it going to my head.

# ALL ABOUT AUGUST

## GOALS FOR AUGUST

_____

_____

_____

_____

_____

_____

_____

_____

_____

_____

_____

## NEW THINGS TO READ/ WATCH/MAKE/EAT

_____

_____

_____

_____

_____

_____

_____

_____

_____

_____

## MUST GET DONE

_____

_____

_____

_____

_____

_____

_____

_____

_____

_____

## SELF-CARE IDEAS

_____

_____

_____

_____

_____

_____

_____

_____

_____

_____

31 MONDAY JULY

1 TUESDAY AUGUST

2 WEDNESDAY

3 THURSDAY

4 FRIDAY

# AUGUST

5 SATURDAY

6 SUNDAY

IMPORTANT BITS

| M | T | W | T | F | S | S |
|---|---|---|---|---|---|---|
| | 1 | 2 | 3 | 4 | 5 | 6 |
| 7 | 8 | 9 | 10 | 11 | 12 | 13 |
| 14 | 15 | 16 | 17 | 18 | 19 | 20 |
| 21 | 22 | 23 | 24 | 25 | 26 | 27 |
| 28 | 29 | 30 | 31 | | | |

7 **MONDAY** AUGUST BANK HOLIDAY

8 TUESDAY

9 WEDNESDAY

10 THURSDAY

11 FRIDAY

## 12 SATURDAY

## 13 SUNDAY

IMPORTANT BITS

| M | T | W | T | F | S | S |
|---|---|---|---|---|---|---|
|   | 1 | 2 | 3 | 4 | 5 | 6 |
| 7 | 8 | 9 | 10 | 11 | 12 | 13 |
| 14 | 15 | 16 | 17 | 18 | 19 | 20 |
| 21 | 22 | 23 | 24 | 25 | 26 | 27 |
| 28 | 29 | 30 | 31 |   |   |   |

14 MONDAY

15 TUESDAY

16 WEDNESDAY

17 THURSDAY

18 FRIDAY

# 19 SATURDAY

# 20 SUNDAY

## IMPORTANT BITS

| M | T | W | T | F | S | S |
|---|---|---|---|---|---|---|
|   | 1 | 2 | 3 | 4 | 5 | 6 |
| 7 | 8 | 9 | 10 | 11 | 12 | 13 |
| 14 | 15 | 16 | 17 | 18 | 19 | 20 |
| 21 | 22 | 23 | 24 | 25 | 26 | 27 |
| 28 | 29 | 30 | 31 |   |   |   |

21 MONDAY

22 TUESDAY

23 WEDNESDAY

24 THURSDAY

25 FRIDAY

## 26 SATURDAY

## 27 SUNDAY

IMPORTANT BITS

| M | T | W | T | F | S | S |
|---|---|---|---|---|---|---|
|   | 1 | 2 | 3 | 4 | 5 | 6 |
| 7 | 8 | 9 | 10 | 11 | 12 | 13 |
| 14 | 15 | 16 | 17 | 18 | 19 | 20 |
| 21 | 22 | 23 | 24 | 25 | 26 | 27 |
| 28 | 29 | 30 | 31 |  |  |  |

28 MONDAY

29 TUESDAY

30 WEDNESDAY

31 THURSDAY

1 FRIDAY SEPTEMBER

# AUGUST

2 SATURDAY

3 SUNDAY

IMPORTANT BITS

| M | T | W | T | F | S | S |
|---|---|---|---|---|---|---|
| | 1 | 2 | 3 | 4 | 5 | 6 |
| 7 | 8 | 9 | 10 | 11 | 12 | 13 |
| 14 | 15 | 16 | 17 | 18 | 19 | 20 |
| 21 | 22 | 23 | 24 | 25 | 26 | 27 |
| 28 | 29 | 30 | 31 | | | |

# AUGUST NOTES

SEPTEMBER

Birthstone: sapphire

Flowers: aster and morning glory

PERSONALITY TRAITS

Practical, kind and thoughtful
describes people born in September,
which is one of the busiest months for
maternity wards after the previous
December's carry-on.

September

| MONDAY | TUESDAY | WEDNESDAY |
|--------|---------|-----------|
| 28 | 29 | 30 |
| 4 | 5 | 6 |
| 11 | 12 | 13 |
| 18 | 19 | 20 |
| 25 | 26 | 27 |
| 2 | 3 | 4 |

| THURSDAY | FRIDAY | SATURDAY | SUNDAY |
|---|---|---|---|
| 31 | 1 | 2 | 3 |
| 7 | 8 | 9 | 10 |
| 14 | 15 | 16 | 17 |
| 21 | 22 | 23 | 24 |
| 28 | 29 | 30 | 1 |
| 5 | 6 | 7 | 8 |

Now that we're in sixth year we get certain privileges, like having a bathroom with hand dryers that actually work and being able to leave the school grounds at lunchtime to watch *Home & Away* in Ciara Quinn's garage.

Of course the best one is running the tuck shop. The proceeds go to our debs fund so it's very high stakes. Since we're hoping to get a band AND a DJ we've put up the price of crisps by 20c and tins of fizzy drinks by 30c. That was my idea, after another successful summer practically running Filan's. There was some pushback from a couple of transition years but otherwise things are going great. Well, they were until Sr Agnes put Tricia Harney in charge of the till on Tuesdays and Thursdays. We don't have any concrete proof, but I have it on good authority (from Majella) that Tricia Harney would take the eye out of your head and come back for the lid. She robbed a pair of runners off Claire Downey at sports day last year and has been brazenly wearing them ever since. Claire swears you can still see where she carved her initials into the soles when Tricia walks through a patch of muck.

'Can someone else not handle the cash?' I begged Sr Agnes. 'I'll do it myself if I have to.'

'With your aptitude for spreadsheets I think you'd be better suited to managing the accounts, Aisling,' she told me. 'I know you're putting teaching and nursing on your CAO form but maybe you should consider something in financial services too.'

I took it as a compliment. But it doesn't take a financial genius to figure out why we haven't made a single cent in profit all week and our float is down by €6. Bloody Tricia Harney!

# ALL ABOUT SEPTEMBER

## GOALS FOR SEPTEMBER

_____

_____

_____

_____

_____

_____

_____

_____

_____

_____

## NEW THINGS TO READ/ WATCH/MAKE/EAT

_____

_____

_____

_____

_____

_____

_____

_____

_____

_____

## MUST GET DONE

_____

_____

_____

_____

_____

_____

_____

_____

_____

_____

## SELF-CARE IDEAS

_____

_____

_____

_____

_____

_____

_____

_____

_____

_____

28 MONDAY AUGUST

29 TUESDAY

30 WEDNESDAY

31 THURSDAY

1 FRIDAY SEPTEMBER

2 SATURDAY

3 SUNDAY

IMPORTANT BITS

| M | T | W | T | F | S | S |
|---|---|---|---|---|---|---|
| | | | | 1 | 2 | 3 |
| 4 | 5 | 6 | 7 | 8 | 9 | 10 |
| 11 | 12 | 13 | 14 | 15 | 16 | 17 |
| 18 | 19 | 20 | 21 | 22 | 23 | 24 |
| 25 | 26 | 27 | 28 | 29 | 30 | |

SEPTEMBER 4–10

4 MONDAY

5 TUESDAY

6 WEDNESDAY

7 THURSDAY

8 FRIDAY INTERNATIONAL LITERACY DAY

# 9 SATURDAY

# 10 SUNDAY

IMPORTANT BITS

| M | T | W | T | F | S | S |
|---|---|---|---|---|---|---|
|   |   |   |   | 1 | 2 | 3 |
| 4 | 5 | 6 | 7 | 8 | 9 | 10 |
| 11 | 12 | 13 | 14 | 15 | 16 | 17 |
| 18 | 19 | 20 | 21 | 22 | 23 | 24 |
| 25 | 26 | 27 | 28 | 29 | 30 |   |

11 MONDAY

12 TUESDAY

13 WEDNESDAY

14 THURSDAY

15 FRIDAY

# 16 SATURDAY

# 17 SUNDAY

IMPORTANT BITS

| M | T | W | T | F | S | S |
|---|---|---|---|---|---|---|
|   |   |   |   | 1 | 2 | 3 |
| 4 | 5 | 6 | 7 | 8 | 9 | 10 |
| 11 | 12 | 13 | 14 | 15 | 16 | 17 |
| 18 | 19 | 20 | 21 | 22 | 23 | 24 |
| 25 | 26 | 27 | 28 | 29 | 30 |   |

18 MONDAY

19 TUESDAY

20 WEDNESDAY

21 **THURSDAY** INTERNATIONAL PEACE DAY

22 FRIDAY

23 SATURDAY

24 SUNDAY

IMPORTANT BITS

| M | T | W | T | F | S | S |
|---|---|---|---|---|---|---|
|  |  |  |  | 1 | 2 | 3 |
| 4 | 5 | 6 | 7 | 8 | 9 | 10 |
| 11 | 12 | 13 | 14 | 15 | 16 | 17 |
| 18 | 19 | 20 | 21 | 22 | 23 | 24 |
| 25 | 26 | 27 | 28 | 29 | 30 |  |

25 MONDAY

26 TUESDAY

27 WEDNESDAY

28 THURSDAY

29 FRIDAY

## 30 SATURDAY

## 1 SUNDAY OCTOBER

IMPORTANT BITS

| M | T | W | T | F | S | S |
|---|---|---|---|---|---|---|
| | | | | 1 | 2 | 3 |
| 4 | 5 | 6 | 7 | 8 | 9 | 10 |
| 11 | 12 | 13 | 14 | 15 | 16 | 17 |
| 18 | 19 | 20 | 21 | 22 | 23 | 24 |
| 25 | 26 | 27 | 28 | 29 | 30 | |

# SEPTEMBER NOTES

OCTOBER

Birthstones: opal and tourmaline

Flowers: marigold and cosmos

October babies grow up to be romantic, intelligent and peace-loving and also get to celebrate their birthday at the turn of Big Coat and Black Tights season.

October

| MONDAY | TUESDAY | WEDNESDAY |
|--------|---------|-----------|
| 25 | 26 | 27 |
| 2 | 3 | 4 |
| 9 | 10 | 11 |
| 16 | 17 | 18 |
| 23 | 24 | 25 |
| 30 | 31 | 1 |

| THURSDAY | FRIDAY | SATURDAY | SUNDAY |
|---|---|---|---|
| 28 | 29 | 30 | 1 |
| 5 | 6 | 7 | 8 |
| 12 | 13 | 14 | 15 |
| 19 | 20 | 21 | 22 |
| 26 | 27 | 28 | 29 |
| 2 | 3 | 4 | 5 |

# AISLING'S DIARY

**13 OCTOBER 2006, AGE 18!**

Last night it was finally my turn to be ceremonially waved into Maguire's by Mikey Maguire as an official eighteen-year-old. He's been serving me for the past year and turning a blind eye but now I won't have to hide in the toilets on the off chance a Garda decides to pay a visit. The whole gang was out and Donie McDonnell asked me to be his girlfriend after two months of us shifting every weekend. I said yes because I've never had an actual boyfriend before, even though Donie is notorious for not standing his round. Majella had a cake for me in the pub and I nearly started crying when I blew out the candles and I don't really know why. Eighteen just feels very old. I opened a savings account last week and got six driving lessons off Mammy and Daddy for my birthday.

We went to the Vortex after Maguire's and Donie held my hand all the way on the minibus. He bought me a drink when we got there in fairness, although I'm pretty sure he drank it himself. I do fancy him, because he has curly hair and brown eyes, but I don't know if he's destined to be the love of my life. Majella took off her bra and aeroplaned it over her head during the *Grease* megamix and nearly got thrown out because the bouncers are 'sick of cleaning up' her bras. I'm not dying too much today, which is good because I have to write an English essay about man's inhumanity to man. Might do it about the Vortex toilets.

# ALL ABOUT OCTOBER

### GOALS FOR
### OCTOBER

### NEW THINGS TO READ/
### WATCH/MAKE/EAT

### MUST GET DONE

### SELF-CARE IDEAS

25 MONDAY SEPTEMBER

26 TUESDAY

27 WEDNESDAY

28 THURSDAY

29 FRIDAY

30 SATURDAY

1 SUNDAY OCTOBER

IMPORTANT BITS

| M | T | W | T | F | S | S |
|---|---|---|---|---|---|---|
|  |  |  |  |  |  | 1 |
| 2 | 3 | 4 | 5 | 6 | 7 | 8 |
| 9 | 10 | 11 | 12 | 13 | 14 | 15 |
| 16 | 17 | 18 | 19 | 20 | 21 | 22 |
| 23 | 24 | 25 | 26 | 27 | 28 | 29 |
| 30 | 31 |  |  |  |  |  |

OCTOBER 2–8

2 MONDAY

3 TUESDAY

4 WEDNESDAY

5 THURSDAY

6 FRIDAY

## 7 SATURDAY

## 8 SUNDAY

IMPORTANT BITS

| M | T | W | T | F | S | S |
|---|---|---|---|---|---|---|
| | | | | | | 1 |
| 2 | 3 | 4 | 5 | 6 | 7 | 8 |
| 9 | 10 | 11 | 12 | 13 | 14 | 15 |
| 16 | 17 | 18 | 19 | 20 | 21 | 22 |
| 23 | 24 | 25 | 26 | 27 | 28 | 29 |
| 30 | 31 | | | | | |

OCTOBER 9–15

9 MONDAY

10 TUESDAY

11 WEDNESDAY

12 THURSDAY

13 FRIDAY

## 14 SATURDAY

## 15 SUNDAY

IMPORTANT BITS

| M | T | W | T | F | S | S |
|---|---|---|---|---|---|---|
| | | | | | | 1 |
| 2 | 3 | 4 | 5 | 6 | 7 | 8 |
| 9 | 10 | 11 | 12 | 13 | 14 | 15 |
| 16 | 17 | 18 | 19 | 20 | 21 | 22 |
| 23 | 24 | 25 | 26 | 27 | 28 | 29 |
| 30 | 31 | | | | | |

16 MONDAY

17 TUESDAY

18 WEDNESDAY

19 THURSDAY

20 FRIDAY

21 SATURDAY

22 SUNDAY

IMPORTANT BITS

| M | T | W | T | F | S | S |
|---|---|---|---|---|---|---|
| | | | | | | 1 |
| 2 | 3 | 4 | 5 | 6 | 7 | 8 |
| 9 | 10 | 11 | 12 | 13 | 14 | 15 |
| 16 | 17 | 18 | 19 | 20 | 21 | 22 |
| 23 | 24 | 25 | 26 | 27 | 28 | 29 |
| 30 | 31 | | | | | |

23 MONDAY

24 TUESDAY

25 WEDNESDAY

26 THURSDAY

27 FRIDAY

# 28 SATURDAY

# 29 SUNDAY

## IMPORTANT BITS

| M | T | W | T | F | S | S |
|---|---|---|---|---|---|---|
| | | | | | | 1 |
| 2 | 3 | 4 | 5 | 6 | 7 | 8 |
| 9 | 10 | 11 | 12 | 13 | 14 | 15 |
| 16 | 17 | 18 | 19 | 20 | 21 | 22 |
| 23 | 24 | 25 | 26 | 27 | 28 | 29 |
| 30 | 31 | | | | | |

30 **MONDAY** OCTOBER BANK HOLIDAY

31 **TUESDAY** HALLOWEEN

1 WEDNESDAY **NOVEMBER**

2 THURSDAY

3 FRIDAY

# OCTOBER

4 SATURDAY

5 SUNDAY

IMPORTANT BITS

| M | T | W | T | F | S | S |
|---|---|---|---|---|---|---|
| | | | | | | 1 |
| 2 | 3 | 4 | 5 | 6 | 7 | 8 |
| 9 | 10 | 11 | 12 | 13 | 14 | 15 |
| 16 | 17 | 18 | 19 | 20 | 21 | 22 |
| 23 | 24 | 25 | 26 | 27 | 28 | 29 |
| 30 | 31 | | | | | |

Birthstone: yellow topaz or citrine

Flower: chrysanthemum

## PERSONALITY TRAITS

If you were born in November you are humble and sweet but can get furious when provoked. You are probably a Valentine's baby so you might want to avoid your parents' eyes next time you see them.

# November

NOVEMBER AT A GLANCE

| MONDAY | TUESDAY | WEDNESDAY |
|--------|---------|-----------|
| 30 | 31 | 1 |
| 6 | 7 | 8 |
| 13 | 14 | 15 |
| 20 | 21 | 22 |
| 27 | 28 | 29 |
| 4 | 5 | 6 |

| THURSDAY | FRIDAY | SATURDAY | SUNDAY |
|---|---|---|---|
| 2 | 3 | 4 | 5 |
| 9 | 10 | 11 | 12 |
| 16 | 17 | 18 | 19 |
| 23 | 24 | 25 | 26 |
| 30 | 1 | 2 | 3 |
| 7 | 8 | 9 | 10 |

I swear to God I've never heard Daddy's voice go so high. I thought my eardrums were going to burst. 'Turn left, Aisling. Lock the wheel! Lock it harder!'

Mammy warned me that asking Daddy to teach me to drive wouldn't end well. But I've used up my six lessons with Pat Smullen and I'm no better off so if I ever want to get my full licence and achieve my dream of owning a Nissan Micra then this is the only way.

The first red flag was when he wanted me to open the bonnet and name the parts of the engine before we did anything else. The second was when he started spraying holy water on the tyres.

'Daddy, I thought we were only going to do a few laps of the front field today? We're not even going on the road.'

'I know,' he said, fastening his seat belt and blessing himself three times, 'but I have my prize Charolais heifers grazing in there. I'm only being careful.'

When I put my hands in the ten and two position and turned the key in the engine I felt all my confidence draining out of me. Of course I've memorised the rules of the road and know what a single yellow line means and how much space to give when you're overtaking a cyclist but when you're actually behind the wheel it's a different story.

'What if I kill someone, Daddy?'

He paled. 'Don't kill one of my heifers, whatever you do. Do you know which pedal is the brake?'

'The middle. ABC.'

He nodded. 'Bring her to the bite point so. Easy, easy. Now gently press down on the accelerator ...' The Massey Ferguson suddenly lurched forward, and that was when the blasted cow jumped out in front of us.

# ALL ABOUT NOVEMBER

## GOALS FOR
## NOVEMBER

_____
_____
_____
_____
_____
_____
_____
_____
_____
_____
_____

## NEW THINGS TO READ/
## WATCH/MAKE/EAT

_____
_____
_____
_____
_____
_____
_____
_____
_____
_____
_____

## MUST GET DONE

_____
_____
_____
_____
_____
_____
_____
_____
_____
_____
_____

## SELF-CARE IDEAS

_____
_____
_____
_____
_____
_____
_____
_____
_____
_____
_____

NOVEMBER 1–5

30 MONDAY OCTOBER

31 TUESDAY

1 WEDNESDAY NOVEMBER ALL SAINTS' DAY

2 THURSDAY

3 FRIDAY

4 SATURDAY

5 SUNDAY

IMPORTANT BITS

| M | T | W | T | F | S | S |
|---|---|---|---|---|---|---|
|   |   | 1 | 2 | 3 | 4 | 5 |
| 6 | 7 | 8 | 9 | 10 | 11 | 12 |
| 13 | 14 | 15 | 16 | 17 | 18 | 19 |
| 20 | 21 | 22 | 23 | 24 | 25 | 26 |
| 27 | 28 | 29 | 30 |   |   |   |

6 MONDAY

7 TUESDAY

8 WEDNESDAY

9 THURSDAY

10 FRIDAY

# 11 SATURDAY

# 12 SUNDAY

## IMPORTANT BITS

| M | T | W | T | F | S | S |
|---|---|---|---|---|---|---|
|   |   | 1 | 2 | 3 | 4 | 5 |
| 6 | 7 | 8 | 9 | 10 | 11 | 12 |
| 13 | 14 | 15 | 16 | 17 | 18 | 19 |
| 20 | 21 | 22 | 23 | 24 | 25 | 26 |
| 27 | 28 | 29 | 30 |   |   |   |

13 MONDAY

14 TUESDAY

15 WEDNESDAY

16 THURSDAY

17 FRIDAY

# 18 SATURDAY

# 19 SUNDAY

IMPORTANT BITS

| M | T | W | T | F | S | S |
|---|---|---|---|---|---|---|
|   |   | 1 | 2 | 3 | 4 | 5 |
| 6 | 7 | 8 | 9 | 10 | 11 | 12 |
| 13 | 14 | 15 | 16 | 17 | 18 | 19 |
| 20 | 21 | 22 | 23 | 24 | 25 | 26 |
| 27 | 28 | 29 | 30 |   |   |   |

20 <sup>MONDAY</sup>

21 <sup>TUESDAY</sup>

22 <sup>WEDNESDAY</sup>

23 <sup>THURSDAY</sup>

24 **FRIDAY** BLACK FRIDAY

# 25 SATURDAY

# 26 SUNDAY

## IMPORTANT BITS

| M | T | W | T | F | S | S |
|---|---|---|---|---|---|---|
| | | 1 | 2 | 3 | 4 | 5 |
| 6 | 7 | 8 | 9 | 10 | 11 | 12 |
| 13 | 14 | 15 | 16 | 17 | 18 | 19 |
| 20 | 21 | 22 | 23 | 24 | 25 | 26 |
| 27 | 28 | 29 | 30 | | | |

NOVEMBER 27–30

---

27 MONDAY

---

28 TUESDAY

---

29 WEDNESDAY

---

30 THURSDAY

---

1 FRIDAY DECEMBER

2 SATURDAY

3 SUNDAY

IMPORTANT BITS

| M | T | W | T | F | S | S |
|---|---|---|---|---|---|---|
| | | 1 | 2 | 3 | 4 | 5 |
| 6 | 7 | 8 | 9 | 10 | 11 | 12 |
| 13 | 14 | 15 | 16 | 17 | 18 | 19 |
| 20 | 21 | 22 | 23 | 24 | 25 | 26 |
| 27 | 28 | 29 | 30 | | | |

# NOVEMBER NOTES

# NOVEMBER NOTES

## DECEMBER

Birthstone: blue topaz or turquoise

Flowers: holly and poinsettia

### PERSONALITY TRAITS

December babies are smarter, tend to
live longer and are very magnanimous,
which must come in handy when
their birthday gets lumped in with
Christmas, present-wise.

December

| MONDAY | TUESDAY | WEDNESDAY |
|--------|---------|-----------|
| 27 | 28 | 29 |
| 4 | 5 | 6 |
| 11 | 12 | 13 |
| 18 | 19 | 20 |
| 25 | 26 | 27 |
| 1 | 2 | 3 |

| THURSDAY | FRIDAY | SATURDAY | SUNDAY |
|---|---|---|---|
| 30 | 1 | 2 | 3 |
| 7 | 8 | 9 | 10 |
| 14 | 15 | 16 | 17 |
| 21 | 22 | 23 | 24 |
| 28 | 29 | 30 | 31 |
| 4 | 5 | 6 | 7 |

# AISLING'S DIARY

I'm absolutely buzzing to go out tonight. Majella is back from her granny's and I'm after getting a new string top in A Wear in the sales. I think I'll wear it with my black flares and borrow Majella's platform mules. I'll probably see Donie out but hopefully it won't be awkward. I'm fairly sure he was going to break up with me anyway so I just beat him to it. He shifted a girl from Knocknamanagh on Stephenses night so he must be grand. I wonder will I have anyone to kiss at midnight?

I must remember to send my Happy New Year texts at ten o'clock so they definitely go through. Mammy and Daddy are gone off to Aunty Sheila's for the evening already and Daddy got me with a 'see you next year' going out the door.

This has been a good year for me, I think. I had my first proper boyfriend and kissed four people. I'm up to second gear in the car and me and Maj went on our first holiday on our own. Tramore was lovely but I'm fairly sure I got lice off the pillows in the B&B.

Everyone'll be out tonight. I wonder will we see that gang from Knock who were in Maguire's for Stephenses night. One of them was very cute. Deirdre Ruane said his name is John, she thinks.

Anyway, that's me signing off for 2006. Fingers crossed that the future brings me lots of love, lads and happiness.

# ALL ABOUT DECEMBER

## GOALS FOR
DECEMBER

_____
_____
_____
_____
_____
_____
_____
_____
_____
_____

## NEW THINGS TO READ/
WATCH/MAKE/EAT

_____
_____
_____
_____
_____
_____
_____
_____
_____
_____

## MUST GET DONE

_____
_____
_____
_____
_____
_____
_____
_____
_____

## SELF-CARE IDEAS

_____
_____
_____
_____
_____
_____
_____
_____
_____

27 MONDAY NOVEMBER

28 TUESDAY

29 WEDNESDAY

30 THURSDAY

1 FRIDAY DECEMBER

# DECEMBER

## 2 SATURDAY

## 3 SUNDAY

## IMPORTANT BITS

| M | T | W | T | F | S | S |
|---|---|---|---|---|---|---|
| | | | | 1 | 2 | 3 |
| 4 | 5 | 6 | 7 | 8 | 9 | 10 |
| 11 | 12 | 13 | 14 | 15 | 16 | 17 |
| 18 | 19 | 20 | 21 | 22 | 23 | 24 |
| 25 | 26 | 27 | 28 | 29 | 30 | 31 |

DECEMBER 4–10

4 MONDAY

5 TUESDAY

6 WEDNESDAY

7 THURSDAY

8 FRIDAY

# 9 SATURDAY

# 10 SUNDAY

## IMPORTANT BITS

| M | T | W | T | F | S | S |
|---|---|---|---|---|---|---|
|   |   |   |   | 1 | 2 | 3 |
| 4 | 5 | 6 | 7 | 8 | 9 | 10 |
| 11 | 12 | 13 | 14 | 15 | 16 | 17 |
| 18 | 19 | 20 | 21 | 22 | 23 | 24 |
| 25 | 26 | 27 | 28 | 29 | 30 | 31 |

11 MONDAY

12 TUESDAY

13 WEDNESDAY

14 THURSDAY

15 FRIDAY

DECEMBER

# 16 SATURDAY

# 17 SUNDAY

IMPORTANT BITS

| M | T | W | T | F | S | S |
|---|---|---|---|---|---|---|
|   |   |   |   | 1 | 2 | 3 |
| 4 | 5 | 6 | 7 | 8 | 9 | 10 |
| 11 | 12 | 13 | 14 | 15 | 16 | 17 |
| 18 | 19 | 20 | 21 | 22 | 23 | 24 |
| 25 | 26 | 27 | 28 | 29 | 30 | 31 |

18 MONDAY

19 TUESDAY

20 WEDNESDAY

21 THURSDAY

22 FRIDAY

# 23 SATURDAY

# 24 SUNDAY CHRISTMAS EVE

IMPORTANT BITS

| M | T | W | T | F | S | S |
|---|---|---|---|---|---|---|
|  |  |  |  | 1 | 2 | 3 |
| 4 | 5 | 6 | 7 | 8 | 9 | 10 |
| 11 | 12 | 13 | 14 | 15 | 16 | 17 |
| 18 | 19 | 20 | 21 | 22 | 23 | 24 |
| 25 | 26 | 27 | 28 | 29 | 30 | 31 |

## DECEMBER 25–31

25 **MONDAY** CHRISTMAS DAY

26 **TUESDAY** ST STEPHEN'S DAY

27 **WEDNESDAY**

28 **THURSDAY**

29 **FRIDAY**

# 30 SATURDAY

# 31 SUNDAY NEW YEAR'S EVE

## IMPORTANT BITS

| M | T | W | T | F | S | S |
|---|---|---|---|---|---|---|
| | | | | 1 | 2 | 3 |
| 4 | 5 | 6 | 7 | 8 | 9 | 10 |
| 11 | 12 | 13 | 14 | 15 | 16 | 17 |
| 18 | 19 | 20 | 21 | 22 | 23 | 24 |
| 25 | 26 | 27 | 28 | 29 | 30 | 31 |

# DECEMBER NOTES

# REFLECTIONS ON 2023

_____

_____

_____

_____

_____

_____

_____

_____

_____

_____

_____

_____

_____

_____

_____

_____

_____

_____

_____

_____

_____

# PRIORITIES FOR 2024